For Mom,
the kindest human I know.

Take a look around and
here is what you'll see,

people just as different
and unique as can be!

Sure, we all look different
but we all feel differently too.

Inside some may feel
shiny and gold

and others may feel blue.

Some days are purple with flecks of red,

and the next may feel pink and green,

the following may feel like a rainbow burst,

and then after, shiny and clean.

These colors
are just emotions
that we all have inside.

Some cause

us to skip

and dance

in joy,

while others push us to hide.

There will be days you feel
just as light as a kite,

there's a bounce in your step and
everything goes right.

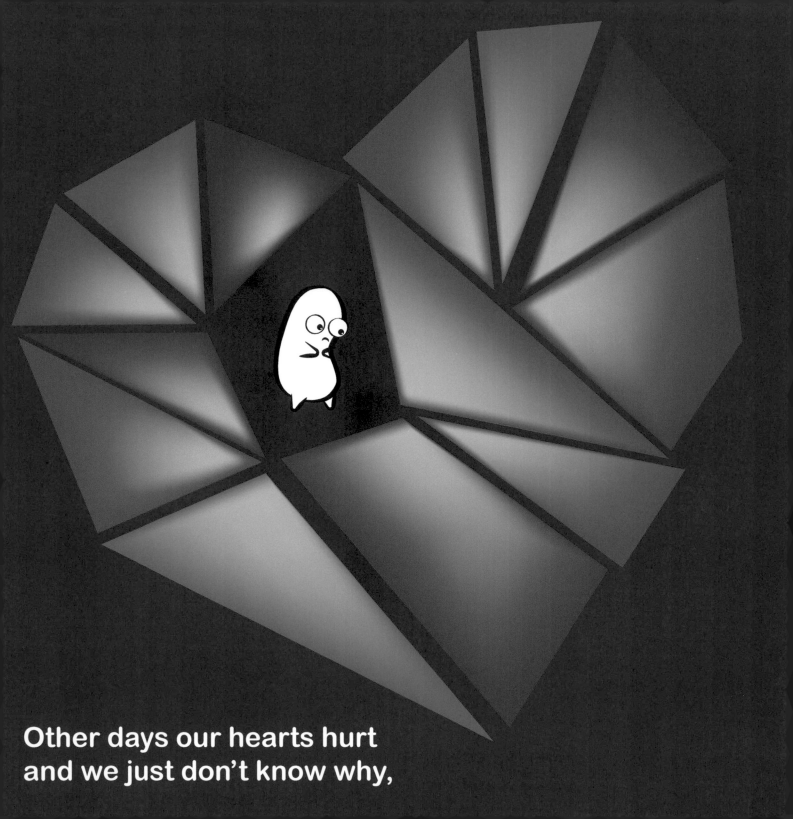

Other days our hearts hurt
and we just don't know why,

like your brain is sort of stuck
and you kind of want to cry.

But no matter how you feel
it is important that you know

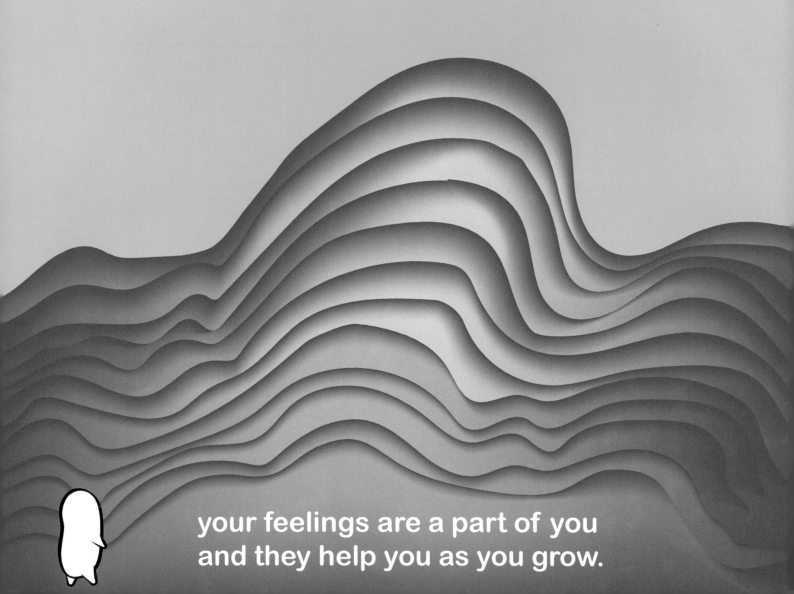

your feelings are a part of you
and they help you as you grow.

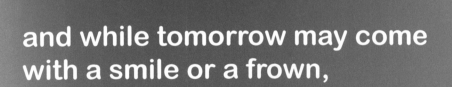

and while tomorrow may come
with a smile or a frown,

there are people who love you,
if you are up or you are down.

Most importantly of all,
know you are not alone.

We are all feeling something,
just not all of it is shown.

So be kind to yourself,

your friends and family too,

be kind to your teachers

and anybody new.

Since we can't know
what's happining
in someone else's mind,

The only real solution…